5. "Er, sorry about that, Worm," said Nellyphant. "Shhh! Don't let Worm see you laughing, Joe," whispered Tiny. "You know how cross he can get."

6. Kind Nellyphant had an idea. "You are too small to play with us, Worm," she said. Then she went indoors and fetched the fish tank. Worm *was* puzzled.

7. Then Nellyphant made a worm-sized diving board and attached it to the fish tank. "The fish won't mind if you play with them, Worm," said Nellyphant.

8. "What a splendid idea!" said Tiny. So, while the big friends splashed about in the big pool, Worm swam with the fish in their fish tank!

Published by IPC Magazines Ltd., King's Reach Tower, Stamford Street, London SE1 9LS, England. Sole Agents for Australia and New Zealand: Gordon & Gotch Ltd.; South Africa: Central News Agency. Printed and bound by Fleetway Printers, Gravesend, Kent.

£2.95

Princess Golden Hair

1. There are always people who want to be different. Princess Golden Hair, who had the most beautiful long, golden hair, was like that. "I'm so tired of having fair hair," she complained. "I wish that it were some other colour. Perhaps blue — or even red!"

2. Then one day, in a workman's hut near the palace, she found a tin of bright red paint! "Now I can have my wish and make my hair into another colour!" laughed Princess Golden Hair. "But first I will put on this old cloak to cover my lovely clothes."

3. Having put on the cloak and daubed her hair with the red paint, Princess Golden Hair went back to the castle. But the guards did not recognise her. "Be off with you, beggar maid!" they boomed. "You cannot enter the palace!" Princess Golden Hair *was* surprised.

4. The more she protested that she was their princess, the more they laughed. "Princess Golden Hair has golden hair like spun sunbeams," they said. "And she wears lovely clothes, not old, paint daubed rags." The guards soon chased Princess Golden Hair away.

5. "Oh, dear, what will become of me?" cried the princess as she rested by a pool. Soon, a young artist found her there. "Seated like that, you make a perfect picture," he smiled. "May I paint your portrait? It will look so pretty." The princess agreed.

6. The artist had no money, but he gave his food to the hungry princess to eat while he painted. "I like this picture of you well enough," he said. "But it would have been perfect if only your hair had been golden, young maiden. What a great pity it is not."

7. "But my hair IS gold!" cried the princess. She told the painter how she had coloured it. "But that is wonderful!" said the artist. Using his paint cleaning fluid, he quickly removed the red paint from her hair. Once again, it was a golden colour.

8. And when the King and Queen came to find Princess Golden Hair, the picture was complete. "It is perfect," said the King to the surprised young artist. "I shall make you the Royal Picture Painter, young man." Later, the painter married the princess.

5

PATCH BRINGS THE COWS HOME

1. Jack and Jill's puppy, Patch, was walking through a nearby field, one day, when he heard a strange high-pitched whistle. It was a shepherd's signal for his dog to begin rounding-up the stray sheep.

2. "What a clever dog!" Patch heard Mr. Barnes, the cowman, say. "I wish I had some help to drive my cows in for milking. I have hurt my leg, you see." Patch gave a sniff and walked back to Buttercup Farm.

3. "I don't know what's so clever about chasing silly sheep!" yapped Patch. "I'm sure I could do it if I tried." Patch practised on the farmyard chickens! What a noise they made as they ran around!

4. "Naughty Patch!" scolded Jack and Jill. "Just look how you've scared the poor chickens!" "Other dogs can chase things and get called *clever,* but if I do it, I get scolded!" grumbled Patch, crossly.

5. Still sulking, Patch went off to a field where the cows grazed. The latch was broken, so Patch was able to walk through the open gate.

6. "I'll go and talk to my friends, the cows," thought Patch. But, as he walked into the field, the cows walked out – through the open gate! "Oh, no!" gasped Patch. "What *have* I done?"

7. Patch knew he would get into trouble for letting the cows out. He ran down the lane after them, barking: "Get back!"

8. But it was milking time and the cows were going into their shed. "Thank you for bringing the cows to me, Patch!" called Mr. Barnes, the cowman. So Jack and Jill didn't scold Patch. In fact, they gave him a big bowl of cool milk.

LOST IN THE SNOW

1.   Bonny and Billy Bunny were going to have tea with their Uncle Bertram. When Mummy had dressed them in their warmest clothes, the bunnies set off.

2.   But on their way to Uncle Bertram's, the bunnies stopped to play in the snow. *"Got you!"* chuckled Bonny, as she hurled a snowballl at Billy.

3.   At last, the bunnies remembered that they were supposed to visit their uncle. They walked on and on – *and on!* After a while, the bunnies stopped.

4.   "I think we're lost!" cried Bonny. "Don't worry, we will go back home again," smiled Billy. But the bunnies didn't know which way *home* was!

5. When Billy saw a sign saying: 'MOLE MOUND', he cheered up again. "This is where Mr. Mole lives," Billy told Bonny. "He lives underground." Billy and Bonny scraped at the snow until they reached a little red door. "There!" said Billy.

6. "Oh, I do hope Mr. Mole is in," sighed Bonny, as Billy tapped on the door. She was beginning to feel cold. Suddenly, the door opened. "Well, come on in, you two," grinned Mr. Mole. "It's too cold to stand out there!"

7. A moment later, Bonny and Billy were seated by the fire in a cosy room. When Mr. Mole heard that they had lost their way — and their tea — he told them they must stay and have tea with him. Bonny and Billy *were* pleased.

8. Later, when Bonny and Billy could eat no more, Mr. Mole gave them some cake for Mummy. Then he took them home. "You will have to go to tea with uncle tomorrow, children," said Mummy, when she heard what had happened.

Leo the Lion

1. Jimmy Mouse and his little friends were holding a contest. "Whichever one of us makes the others laugh most, wins that lovely hat," Jimmy told Leo the lion.

2. "I'll make you all laugh!" said Leo. He tried to copy Monty Mole and did a handstand. "Look out! Leo's going to fall on us!" shouted Jimmy's friends.

3. THUMP! Leo tumbled over, just missing the other animals. "Silly lion!" scolded Monty. "You didn't make us laugh, at all. Play somewhere else!"

4. Poor Leo crept away. But as he went off, his tail tickled Monty. "Oh, stop it!" giggled Monty. "Hey, Leo. You are making Monty laugh!" chuckled Jimmy.

5. "I am?" grinned Leo. Suddenly, he swished his tail and began tickling the other little animals, too. They laughed so much, they couldn't stand up!

6. "Well, you certainly win the prize for making us all laugh, Leo!" said Jimmy and his friends, when Leo had stopped tickling them. Leo *did* feel proud.

The little fox

Long ago, there was a little fox who lived in a room at the very top of a castle. From a window, the fox could see all that was happening in the village far below. Now one day, the fox, who could work magic, watched as the bad Baron rode into the village. "I'm very fierce and I am going to be unkind to EVERYBODY!" chuckled the Baron. "I think I'd better have a word with that naughty Baron," thought the little fox. So he wished hard – and the Baron appeared in the room, scratching his head. When he saw the fox, he boomed: "I'm very fierce and I'm going to chase you!" "No, you are not," smiled the fox. "If you were fierce, the villagers would not cheer you. Look outside." They looked out of the window and saw "THREE CHEERS FOR THE BARON" written on a big banner. What the Baron could not see, was that the villagers had written "THREE CHEERS FOR THE BARON'S HORSE." Only the last part was hidden. You see, the Baron's horse was giving the village children rides around the market place, and that was why the village people were cheering. "Well, as everybody thinks I'm such a nice, pleasant fellow, I suppose I shall have to start acting like one," said the Baron, looking rather pleased with himself. "After all, I don't want to upset folk." "Of course, you don't," grinned the fox, who had read *all* of the message on the banner. So, from that day on, the bad Baron became known as the *good Baron*. Quite often, when the fox looked out of his window, he could see the Baron helping children on to his horse and leading them round the market place. "It just goes to show you what can happen if only people would always say nice things to each other," thought the fox. Which is quite true, isn't it?

Teddy Bear and

1. Teddy Bear's grandma had invited all the bears who live in Bear Green, to an Easter party at her house. "We must hurry, we don't want to be late," said Teddy, as he and his mummy and daddy set off for Grandma's house. "We won't be. Slow down!" grinned Daddy.

2. "Come and give your grandma a big kiss, Teddy," said Grandma, when he and Mummy and Daddy arrived at the party. "Er, I have an Easter present for you, Grandma," said Teddy, as he handed her a parcel. "I hope you like it." Teddy was feeling embarrassed.

3. Well, Grandma was delighted with her present, a pretty scarf Teddy had chosen himself. But instead of giving Teddy a present, too, as Teddy had thought she would, Grandma went off to put the scarf away. Then Twinkle, Grandma's cat, came to say, "Hello!"

4. A few minutes later, Ivan and Hill Billy arrived with an Easter egg for Grandma. Soon the door bell rang again and Grandma hurried out. "I wonder what Grandma will give us?" whispered Ivan and Hill Billy. "Grandma *did* say she had a present for each of us."

the Easter Party

5.   Well, Grandma had just brought Bare Bear and Grizzly into the room, when something funny happened. Twinkle came out from under an armchair and he was patting a little Easter egg! "Look what Twinkle has found!" gasped the bears. Grandma wagged a finger.

6.   "Oh, that mischievous kitten!" she grinned. "He has spoilt my surprise for you all." Then Grandma explained why she hadn't given the bears any presents. She had hidden them in the living-room! "But why have you *hidden* our presents, Grandma?" asked Teddy.

7.   "I thought it would be more fun if you had to find the presents," smiled Grandma. "Oh, yes, it *would!*" said Teddy. The other bears thought so, too. Soon, everyone was searching round the room for an Easter egg each. "I've found an Easter egg!" called Teddy.

8.   Soon, all the other bears had found Easter eggs, too. "This is the nicest Easter party we have ever had," said all the bears. "The best part is yet to come," said Grandma. She was right. The bears all sat down and had a lovely Easter tea that Grandma had made.

13

THE KITCHEN PIRATES

Tiger Tim found a leaking kitchen water pipe, one day. "I'll tell the plumber to come," he told Mrs. Bruin, as she went out shopping. But naughty Tim told the plumber to come along at tea-time! What fun the Bruin Boys had until then! They let the kitchen start to fill up with water – and played PIRATES! Poor Mrs. Bruin could hardly believe her eyes, when she looked in at the window, later, and saw her boys!

Now look carefully at the picture above and try to find six sponges hidden in it.

The boys had to use them to mop up the mess after the plumber had been.

The Princess Who Could Not Laugh

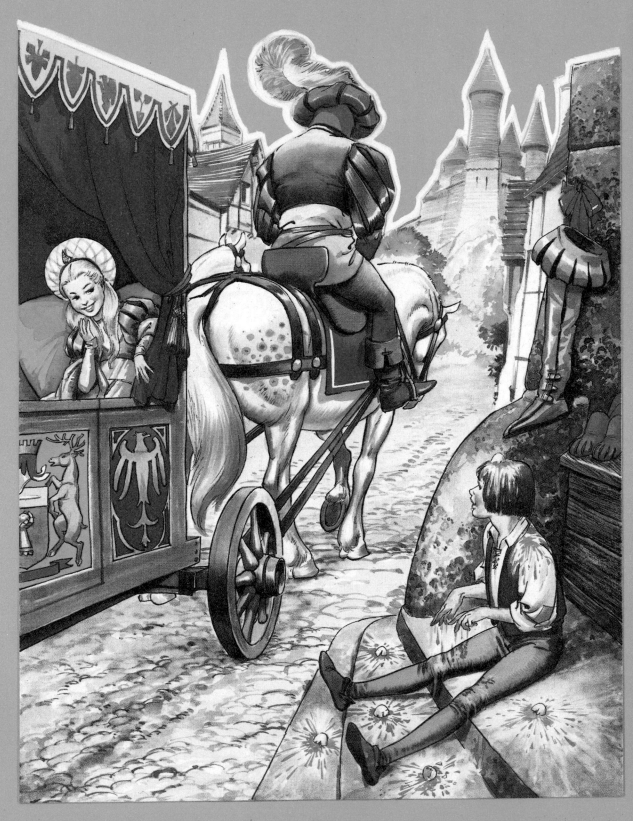

ONCE UPON A TIME, long ago there was a princess whose name was Rose. Princess Rose lived with her mummy and daddy in a lovely palace.

She was a very lucky girl. She had lots of toys, a nice garden to play in and her very own pony.

But there was one thing that Princess Rose did not have. That thing was a laugh. She wasn't unhappy, she wasn't lonely, she just could not laugh.

"It is very worrying," said the King. "All children should laugh."

Anyway, the King decided to offer a prize to anyone who could make his daughter laugh. He put notices all over his kingdom saying: *To anyone who can make my daughter laugh I will grant them anything they wish, signed, The King.*

Well, when people read that notice they came to the palace, thinking they could easily make Princess Rose laugh. But they were wrong.

Even though the King and Queen sat laughing at nearly everyone who came, Princess Rose just sat there, without even smiling.

It was all very strange.

Anyway, living in the same palace was a young kitchen boy named Tim.

His job was to run errands for the palace cook. He had to fetch the shopping, keep the kitchen clean, peel potatoes, wash up and do any other chores that the cook wanted him to do.

"Tim, fetch me that spoon," ordered the cook. "Tim, get some salt. Tim, find me my apron."

Poor Tim scampered round the kitchen doing as he was told.

Tim knew about Princess Rose and felt sorry that she could not laugh. He had seen her playing in the garden with the other children, and although the others were laughing Rose seemed so sad.

One day, the cook called out to Tim, "Go to the the village and fetch me some eggs. Hurry boy, the King wants scrambled eggs."

Tim raced down to the village. The man in the shop put the eggs in a bag, and Tim started back to the palace. He was in such a hurry that he didn't see a coach coming up the road. Suddenly a voice called out, "Look out, you stupid boy."

Tim nearly jumped out of his skin, as he saw the coach coming towards him.

He jumped on the pavement, slipped and fell over. Up into the air went the eggs, then down they came again, splop, splop, splop — all over Tim.

Tim sat on the pavement, feeling a bit worried. What was he going to tell the cook?

Suddenly he heard someone laughing.

When he looked up, he saw Princess Rose sitting in the carriage, laughing.

Tears were rolling down her cheeks as she laughed and laughed!

"I am sorry," said the Princess. "But the way you jumped out of the way and the eggs landing on you, it was so funny. Oh ho, ho."

Well, as you can imagine, the King heard how Tim had made his daughter laugh and he was very pleased.

He summoned Tim to his room.

"For making my daughter laugh, you may have anything you wish," he told the surprised kitchen boy.

Tim thought for a moment. Then he said, "What I would like most of all, would be to play in the garden with the Princess on my day off."

The King was amazed.

"Wouldn't you sooner have money, riches, a palace?" he said.

But Tim said he wanted to play with the princess. "You see," he said " she has the prettiest laugh I have ever heard!"

HAROLD and his

1. "Lets go for a nice walk to the shops," said Dicky Dormouse, one day. "Er, no – I'd rather go by car," said lazy Harold. "Buttercup could do with some exercise." But Harold's little yellow car, Buttercup, looked an awful mess when Harold looked into the garage.

2. "We can't go out in Buttercup until she is clean and shiny all over," said Harold, dashing back into the house. "Whatever would people think?" Dicky couldn't help smiling when he saw funny Harold wearing his cleaning and shining outfit. *Very smart!* Dicky giggled.

3. "Now for a wash, with plenty of splosh!" sang Harold, as he rubbed and scrubbed at Buttercup with lots of soapflakes, water and bath salts. Dicky set to work cleaning the inside of the car with a Dicky-sized broom. "Almost finished now," smiled Harold.

4. When Buttercup was dry, topsy-turvy Harold put plenty of polish on. Then when the polish had been polished, he gave Buttercup's bonnet a quick going over with the vacuum cleaner! Just look at the mess Harold made as he polished and cleaned his car.

clean motor car

5. At last, Buttercup was as clean and shiny as a brand new car. "Now we can go off to Leafy Wood shops," said Harold, as he put on his very best driving clothes. "About time, too!" joked Dicky. "I thought you would be cleaning Buttercup all afternoon!"

6. "Golly showers!" Harold suddenly cried out. Poor Dicky nearly jumped out of his fur. *What's wrong?* Dicky stuttered. *"Rain!* That's what's wrong!" sighed Harold, as a black cloud passed overhead. Then it began to rain – harder and harder. Harold *was* upset.

7. Instead of whizzing off to Leafy Wood with Dicky, Harold pushed his car back into the garage just as fast as he could push! "You naughty rain!" Harold said. "You are wrong if you think you are going to make my lovely, shining car, wet all over!"

8. "Now that Buttercup has been cleaned, she can jolly well *stay* clean," said the funny hare. "I'll never quite get used to Harold's strange ways," Dicky thought to himself, as they both walked to the shops through the pouring rain. "What a funny day!" giggled Dicky.

Edward and the Jumblies

1.   Edward is a little boy who lives with his mummy and daddy in Jumbly Land. One day, Edward's daddy made Edward, the King and the Jumblies kites to play with. "What fun we will all have with these!" said the Jumblies.

2.   But Daddy didn't have any string to put on kites. So the King said he would buy some from the String Shop. "I'm very sorry," said the Shop Jumbly. "The Bundly Bing bought all my string." Edward and the Jumblies did look sad.

3.   "Who is The Bundly Bing?" Edward asked. "I don't know," said the King. "But I know where he lives. We'll go and ask him for some string." On their way, Edward saw a notice tied with string saying: *To the Bundly Bing.*

4.   And what a surprise they all had when they saw the house of the Bundly Bing! It was all held together with *string!* "Goodness me!" gasped Edward. "What a strange Jumbly." "I have never seen anything like it!" said the King.

5. The friends had an even bigger surprise when they went into the house. Sitting on a table, held together with string, was the Bundly Bing. "What *is* he doing?" whispered Edward, as they watched the Bundly Bing tying himself up with lots of string.

6. "Er, why are you doing that?" asked the King. "Because I *like* doing it, of course!" said the Bundly Bing. Then the King asked for some string. "You can have as much as you like. I have plenty," smiled the Bundly Bing. "We can see that!" laughed the Jumblies.

7. So Edward and the Jumblies took a ball of string each from a big boxful. "Thank you very much," they said. "Now we can fly our kites." They left the Bundly Bing happily tying more string round himself. "He may be strange, but he's quite a nice chap," said the King.

8. What a lovely time Edward and the Jumblies had flying their kites, that afternoon. "Come on wind, make my kite fly higher!" chuckled the King. "If it flies any higher, it will disappear into that big cloud!" said Edward, as his kite dipped and sawed.

Freddie's plant

1. Freddie Frog, who lives in Bumble Down, is always having wonderful ideas. "Oh, I must buy that!" chuckled Freddie, when he saw a house plant for sale. But Terry Tortoise looked worried.

2. "I'll really look after this plant," smiled Freddie. "And I'll help it grow by buying some special plant food." "I'm not sure I really want that plant in our house," said Terry. "It's *huge!*"

3. Well, Freddie kept the house plant on a stool in the living-room. He fed it with plant food every morning and every evening. "It will soon be the finest plant ever!" said Freddie.

4. That plant grew and grew, until it took up more room than anything else in the room. "This plant will have to go in the garden," frowned Terry. "It is far too big to stay indoors!"

5. Terry made Freddie help him carry it outside. They put the plant next to the tool shed. "The plant will help to hide our rickety old tool shed, anyway," Terry told Freddie Frog.

6. Freddie dug a deep hole and Terry lowered the plant over him so that he could put the roots firmly in the ground. Suddenly, Freddie whooped with delight. "I have a wonderful idea!" he laughed.

7. "This house plant has changed into a plant house! We can pull down our old shed and put everything in here!" said Freddie. Freddie's and Terry's nephews loved the new plant house, too.

8. It didn't take Freddie long to carry the gardening tools into the new *garden shed.* "I knew it was a good idea to buy a house plant," chuckled Freddie. The nephews thought so, too.

PADDY-PAWS at the Seaside

1. Mummy and Daddy have taken Little Master and his puppy, Paddy-Paws, to the seaside. "Come on, Paddy, let's build a sandcastle!" called Master, as he and Paddy raced along the beach.

2. Well, Paddy would rather have played a ball game with Master. But, like a good puppy, he sat and watched as Master built a huge sandcastle. "Very nice, son!" called Daddy, as he watched.

3. At last, Master finished building his sandcastle. "Now what shall we do, Paddy?" he asked. "Please can we play a ball game?" woofed Paddy. Master guessed what Paddy was trying to say.

4. "Here, fetch it, boy!" said Master, picking up the ball and throwing it as far as he could. "Ah, this is a much better game," thought Paddy, as he scampered along the sandy beach.

5. Master threw the ball quite a way. Along the beach it bounced — and *bounced!* Paddy was enjoying chasing the ball so much, he didn't notice that it was bouncing towards the sea. SPLASH!

6. Into the sea went the ball — and right behind it went Paddy! Usually Paddy hates water. What a nasty shock he got when a big wave swished over him as he picked up the ball.

7. Little Master couldn't help laughing when he saw Paddy. The bedraggled pup still had the ball in his mouth as he walked towards Master with a piece of soggy seaweed hanging from his head!

8. But it was Paddy who had the last laugh. "I'll make you wet, too!" he woofed. Paddy shook himself hard, so water sprayed all over Master. "Well, I asked for that!" chuckled Master.

TEDDY'S party puzzles

1. Join up all the dots to finish drawing this New Year cake. Then colour the cake with your paints or colouring pencils. The cake is for Teddy and his friends.

2. These six jellies on a plate all look the same. But two pictures are different from the others. Say which two.

3. Teddy and his friends played lots of games at their New Year party. One game was called *Hunt-the-slipper.* How many slippers can you find hidden in the picture?

4. Teddy and Bare Bear are playing musical chairs. Which line must they choose to reach the chair?

5. Shade in the parts marked B-blue, R-red and BK-black, to see what is in the presents.

LEO THE LION GETS HICCUPS

Poor Leo the lion! No matter how hard he tried, he just could not stop *hic-hic-hiccuping!* "Hold your breath and count to twenty," said his little friend, Jimmy Mouse. But Leo only managed to count to five and — HIC! He was off again! Jimmy had an idea. Very quietly, he climbed to the top of a tree near where Leo was sitting. Then he threw a coconut on to the ground, as hard as he could — *crack!* Jimmy thought the loud noise would give Leo a scare and stop him hiccuping. But it didn't work. While Leo was still hiccuping, Jimmy crept away with the broken coconut shell. "I'll paint a face on the coconut shell and give Leo a bigger fright!" Jimmy thought to himself. Funny Jimmy put the painted shell over his body, then climbed on to two stilts he had made. But as he walked towards Leo, making strange noises, Leo just hic-hiccuped, then looked away! "All this horrid hiccuping

has – *hic* – made me too tired to – *hic* – be frightened of a silly – *hic* – monster!'' hiccuped Leo. "And anyway, I know it's you under that coconut mask, Jimmy!" But suddenly, Leo found the energy to jump up and race towards his friend. Jimmy couldn't see through the coconut mask – and was walking towards the edge of the cliff-top! "STOP! Oh, *please* stop!" roared Leo, as he ran towards his friend. "You will go over the top of the cliff, Jimmy!" But Jimmy couldn't hear a thing underneath the mask. "Oh my goodness. What shall I do?" gasped Leo. Now, Leo isn't a very brave lion, as his friends well know. But, when it came to trying to save his little friend, Leo didn't hesitate. He hurled himself forward and tried to catch Jimmy before he fell. Too late, Jimmy and Leo went over the top of the cliff! "Don't worry, I'll save you!" cried Leo, as he rolled over and over. Leo landed at the bottom of the cliff with a *thump!* Luckily, he wasn't hurt. "Help!" cried Jimmy. Leo stretched out his paws and caught Jimmy just in time. "You *are* a brave lion, after all, Leo!" beamed Jimmy, as Leo held him in his paws. "And have you noticed, all that excitement has stopped you hiccuping!" "Well, so it has!" laughed Leo. "It looks like we have both helped each other today, Jimmy. But I don't think I'll hurl myself over the side of a cliff to stop myself hiccuping next time! I'll try something a little safer." "Yes, perhaps you are right," grinned Jimmy. "After all, if you became *too* brave, you wouldn't need me to look after you, Leo!" "That will *never* happen. I will always need you, Jimmy!" purred Leo.

the circus cake

Mandy's form mistress asked every girl and boy in her class to make something special for the school Summer Fair. "We want our stall to sell lots of things, to get money for the new school swimming pool, children," she told everyone. Mandy thought and thought. "What *should* I make?" she wondered. Well, her mummy had taught her how to make cakes. So why not make a nice cake for the class stall? Back home, Mandy asked her mummy if she could have some flour, butter and eggs. Then she made a lovely jam sponge. Of course, Mummy helped Mandy to put the cake in the hot oven, so she wouldn't burn herself. When the sponge had been taken out of the oven and left to cool for a while, Mandy wound a strip of marzipan around the edge. Then she placed some small circus toys on the top of the cake, so that it looked like a circus ring. When Mandy took her cake to school the next day, everyone thought it was lovely. "Hide it before I get too hungry!" said Matthew, with a cheeky grin. All sorts of things had been made for the class stall, but no-one else had baked a cake! "Very nice," said the form mistress, as she collected everything for the senior girls to arrange on the stalls. The next day was Summer Fair Day! But when she looked, Mandy's cake wasn't on the class stall. Her cake had been put on the Cake Competition stall, amongst the older girls' entries!

"There has been a mistake!" gasped Mandy. "I must tell our form teacher, Miss Dawn, right away!" But it was too late. The school gates had been opened and people were streaming into the grounds, admiring the decorations and the beautiful things on show. Poor Mandy *did* look sad as she helped to make tea for the school visitors. "I must try not to cry, I really must!" sobbed Mandy, as she wiped a tear from her cheek. But for her, the wonderful day was spoilt. *Her* cake, her lovely cake was on the wrong stall. "I wish I could go home," thought Mandy, as she tried her hardest to look cheerful. It was quite a time later that the Cake Judging began — and quite a time after that when the Headmistress stepped forward to declare the winner. "All the entries are splendid," she said. "But one cake is *so* different from the rest. It is a Circus Cake. I award it the First Prize. As it does not have a name on it, will the pupil who made it, please step forward?" What a surprise everyone had when Mandy stepped forward. "Well done, my dear," the

headmistress beamed, handing Mandy an envelope with two one pound notes in it. How the visitors and children clapped. Mandy put the money towards her class's stall money — which helped make it the largest amount made by any class in the school. "And it is all thanks to your splendid Circus Cake, Mandy," smiled Miss Dawn. Mandy was sure that it was the happiest day of her life. "I'll never be this happy again!" she said, trying to hold back the tears, once again.

Katie's café

Katie Country Mouse lives in Bluebell Down. Other little friends who live nearby, often visit Katie because she is always so kind and helpful. One day, Peter and Penelope Pinky Mouse showed Katie a book they had found in the Big World. "My, this looks interesting," said Katie, as she read the title on the book cover. "What does it say?" asked Peter and Penelope excitedly. "It says..." said Katie, *"Happy Holiday Guide."* Katie climbed up a ladder and turned the first page of the book. There she saw a picture of a Self Service Cafeteria. "This picture has given me a wonderful idea!" smiled Katie, as she stepped off the ladder. "I wonder what Katie's idea is?" whispered Penelope. "We shall just have to wait and find out," grinned Peter, as Katie rushed off to visit Monty Mole, the Bluebell Down Carpenter. Katie's friend, Hilary Hamster, was in charge of the Bluebell Down Cafe, you see. But the cafe was being redecorated and it looked as if the job would take quite a long time before it was finished. So Katie asked Monty Mole to help cut away at those pages of Peter and Penelope's book, to make a nice space inside. Then Katie asked lots of her friends to help carry all the waste paper away. It was very hard work because the book was rather large – and Katie's helpers were all rather small. It seemed as though there were enough pieces of paper to fill all the waste paper baskets in the world! It didn't take Hilary long to see what Katie's clever idea was. And it didn't take the Bluebell Down folk long to make that idea come true. Katie's idea was to make a little house for Hilary from that book – a cafe house with a

self-service counter! As soon as it was ready, Hilary brought along lots of things to eat and drink. Soon, all the Bluebell Down folk were helping themselves to what they wanted. Then they went up a little ladder to the pretty roof garden. "This must be one of the best – and cleverest ideas you have ever had, Katie!" smiled Hilary, as Katie sat drinking a cup of tea at her own special table. "Nice of you to say so," said Katie, trying hard not to blush. But she did feel rather proud.

THE SOLDIER AND THE ELF

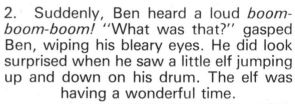

1. There was once a soldier drummer-boy named Ben, who decided to go off in search of a fortune. After travelling for many days, the weary drummer-boy put down his drum and sat under the shade of a tree. He was soon fast asleep.

2. Suddenly, Ben heard a loud *boom-boom-boom!* "What was that?" gasped Ben, wiping his bleary eyes. He did look surprised when he saw a little elf jumping up and down on his drum. The elf was having a wonderful time.

3. "If you dance so hard, you will go right through the skin of my drum," smiled Ben, as he gently held the elf in the palm of one hand. "Please let me go!" pleaded the elf. "If you do, I will show you where there is treasure."

4. "Well now, I must admit, I could do with some treasure right now," smiled Ben. "My pockets are empty." The kind elf led Ben to a miserable and very weedy-looking orchard. "Is *this* the treasure?" asked Ben.

5. The elf smiled. "If you dig between the trees, not too far, not too near, not too shallow and not too deep, you will find treasure," said the elf. So the drummer-boy took off his coat and began to dig. It was very hard work.

6. For days and days he worked. The days turned into weeks and the trees blossomed and fruit appeared. But still Ben could not find any of the promised treasure. "The elf must have lied to me," Ben decided, at last.

7. In the end, Ben gave up digging and picked all the fruit off the trees, which he then took to market. To his surprise, the fruit sold very quickly. People rushed to buy it — and then came back for more, again and again!

8. "I have found the treasure at last!" said the drummer-boy. "This is what the little elf meant all the time. There is *always* treasure to be found if you are willing to work hard for it. I have learned something important!"

Fliptail the Otter

He lives by a stream in Bramble Wood.

1. Fliptail the otter went to visit his special friend, Debbie, one day. She was looking at a bush in her garden. "This is a butterfly bush. All the butterflies come to see it," she smiled.

2. "Come and see Debbie's butterfly bush – it's lovely!" Fliptail told his friends, when he went back to Bramble Wood, that evening. "There are so many beautiful butterflies to see!"

3. But Fliptail's friends looked upset when they went to Debbie's garden to see the magic butterfly bush. All the butterflies had gone away to sleep. "Fliptail has tricked us!" they said.

4. "There is no such thing as a silly *butterfly bush*!" said a squirrel, as he and his woodland friends ran home. Then Joe, the lamp-lighter, came into the village to light the street lamps.

5.   Gas lights are still used in Bramble Wood village, you see. Suddenly, as Joe lit a lamp, a moth fluttered round the bright lamps. "Look!" Fliptail said to his friend, Robin Redbreast.

6.   While Joe lit the other street lamps, Fliptail and Robin ran to their woodland friends. "Follow me!" called Fliptail, excitedly. "I have a wonderful sight to show you all."

7.   The woodland friends followed the otter back to the street lamp. There they saw lots of beautiful moths fluttering round the bright light. "Oh, how wonderful!" they squealed.

FLIPTAIL'S ANIMAL FRIENDS

Zebras, like the two on the right, live on the grassy plains of Africa. They are quite shy but, when animals attack them, they will kick out with their legs to protect themselves.

Being helpful

1. Ben's mummy and daddy always seem to be doing things indoors. So, when he can, Ben likes to help them. One day, when Mummy had washed the dirty dishes, Ben helped by drying them for her.

2. When Ben had dried the last dish, he went outside. Daddy had just arrived home from work and had parked his car in the driveway. ''My goodness! Daddy's car looks like it has been driven through a coal shed!'' thought Ben, when he saw the car. ''I will clean the car and give Daddy a nice surprise.''

3. Ben soon found a bucket in the garage. He filled it with water from the garden tap, then went indoors for something else he needed. ''If Mummy uses washing powder to make her dishes sparkle,'' thought Ben. ''Then I'll have to use lots and lots of this washing powder to make Daddy's car clean, too.'' He poured *all* the powder into the bucket!

4. "Now to start work," smiled Ben, as he dipped a sponge into the soapy water. He was soon swishing the sponge over the car. The more Ben rubbed at the paintwork with his soapy sponge, the more big bubbles appeared. "I've almost finished now," grinned Ben. He looked very pleased with himself.

5. But when Daddy came up, *he* didn't look very pleased, at all! "What *are* you trying to do, Ben?" gasped Daddy. "I can hardly see my car for all these bubbles!" "I'm trying to wash your car," said Ben. "I thought I was making a good job of it, too!"

6. "Well yes, you have," smiled Daddy. "I think you have used too much washing powder, though." "Yes, so do I!" grinned Ben. But kind Daddy let Ben wash all the bubbles off his car with water from the garden hose. Then, when the car was nice and dry, Ben helped Daddy to polish it. "Well done!" Mummy and Daddy told Ben, later. "You *have* been helpful today!"

Esmerelda Witch is always getting herself into one kind of trouble or another. One day, she decided to visit her friend, Wendy Witch, who lives in a big town. "Come on, wake up, you lazy thing!" Esmerelda told her cat, Cleo. "We're going visiting!" Cleo looked up at Esmerelda and groaned: "Not again! The last time we visited Wendy Witch, we lost our way — and had to ask another cat for directions. I *did* feel silly." "Not this time," grinned Esmerelda. "I have planned this trip very carefully." Esmerelda and Cleo climbed on to their magic flying broomstick and off they went. Soon they were flying over tall buildings. "We must be nearly there now," said Cleo. "Almost — I *think*," said Esmerelda. "THINK?" Cleo grumbled "What do you mean, you *think*? Don't you *know* where we are?" "Yes, yes, of course I do. We just have to go round this cloud roundabout and then . . ." began Esmerelda. Before she had a chance to finish what she was saying, an angry voice chirped: "Hey! Watch where you are going!" "Er, sorry," gasped Esmerelda. "I didn't see you there." "Didn't see us?" squawked a pigeon. "If your eyesight is that bad, you shouldn't be driving a magic broomstick!" "I knew something like this would happen. I just *knew* it!" mumbled Cleo. "I think we should report you to the air traffic controller for dangerous driving!" said another pigeon. "They will take your broomstick driving licence away." "Oh, I really *am* sorry," said Esmerelda. "Please forget that you ever saw me." "No,

I'm afraid we can't do that," said another pigeon. "On our way home, we will report you to the air police." Esmerelda thought fast. "If I lose my broomstick driving-licence, Cleo and I will NEVER get back home," she sighed to herself. "I'll just have to make these pigeons forget they ever saw me." She snapped her fingers and said a magic spell. Suddenly, the pigeons fluttered around in circles, looking very puzzled. Before the spell had time to wear off, Esmerelda steered her broomstick towards home. "We will have to visit Wendy another time, Cleo," she said.

But Esmerelda saw her friend, Wendy, much sooner than she thought she would! As she steered her broomstick around a sharp bend, Esmerelda toppled off her broomstick. Luckily, she didn't fall far. She landed feet-first on a weather vane on top of a church spire. When Wendy Witch saw a figure standing on the church spire, she guessed it was her friend, at once, and came to rescue her. "I knew something like this could only happen to you, Esmerelda," grinned Wendy.

Esmerelda and the Pigeons

Fun in Toyland

Archie Aeroplane was so excited, he could hardly stop his wings from flapping. You see, it was the day of the Toyland Aeroplane Race – and Archie loves races. "I'm going to win this race!" thought Archie. Suddenly, Mr. Starter waved the starting flag – and the race began! But Archie is only a little aeroplane and he is *not* very speedy. Whizzy Rocket and the others were soon whizzing ahead of him! "They have such powerful engines!" spluttered Archie. "But I might win yet, if I really try my very hardest." But, when Archie came near the finishing post, he saw all the other aeroplanes were already there. "*Oh, dear!*" he groaned. "I *did* want to be the winner – just for once!" Archie started to land, but he was so sad that he didn't notice when one of his tyres popped! Archie managed to land quite safely, as you can see, but the popped tyre made him skid along the ground. Soon, Archie was zig-zagging round some little posts. The posts had been put there for the Toy Car Race. Poor Archie had no idea what they were for. All he knew for sure was that he *couldn't* stop! "Look out, everyone!" he cried. "I, er, think it's going to take me a while to stop myself." Archie whizzed on and

Toyland is a lovely place to live. All the toys who live there do exciting things. Here is a story all about the time a little aeroplane named Archie went in for the Toyland Aeroplane Race. Poor Archie. It isn't easy to win an aeroplane race when you are smaller than all the others. Funny Archie manages to win a race, though, but not the one he went in for, as you will see.

on – *and on!* He splashed through a big, wet puddle. "Why don't you look where you are going?" called a very cross-looking car. "You have made me wet!" "I think this is going to be one of my unlucky days," sighed poor Archie. But it was really Archie's *lucky* day, although he didn't know it yet. As he sped on, he passed lots of toys who cheered and waved to him. "Well done, Archie!" they called. "What *can* be happening?" thought Archie. Suddenly, he bumped into a large bale of hay and came to a grinding halt. The hay had been put there to stop cars, but it stopped Archie, too. Archie just couldn't believe his ears when Tommy the toy soldier raced up to him and said: "Archie, you have won the Toy Car Race!" Without knowing it, Archie had been speeding along the Car Race Track! "You are the winner!" said the King, giving Archie a garland of flowers. "I know that you are not a car, but you ran along the ground just like one!" "Well, I wanted to win a race – and it looks like I have, doesn't it?" grinned Archie. "What a clever chap I am!" After having his burst tyre replaced, kind Archie took the Toyland children for a lovely ride.

NUTTY NODDLE

1. Aunt Scofalot had invited Nutty Noddle to tea. "I'd better hurry, otherwise Aunty will have eaten all the food!" thought Nutty, as he pulled his tricycle out of the garden shed. By now, it was raining quite hard.

2. "I wish this rain wouldn't go in my eyes," sighed Nutty, as he pedalled along the High Street. Luckily, he was wearing his rain clothes. But he could not see where he was going – and almost knocked over a pedestrian!

3. "This is no good. It's dangerous to drive if you can't see where you are going," thought Nutty. He climbed off his cycle and pushed it home again. Then he ran indoors to fetch his big umbrella. Now he would be able to see.

4. But Nutty had to hold the umbrella with one hand – and steer his cycle with the other hand! *"Ooooer!"* gasped Nutty, as his cycle began to wobble. "Look where you are going!" called a man, as Nutty wobbled towards him.

5. "Well, that wasn't such a good idea, after all!" grumbled Nutty, as he pulled up to a curb. Suddenly, he saw a sign in a shop window. It said: 'SMALL TENT. CHEAP'. "That's what *I* need!" said Nutty, rushing into the shop.

6. The shop salesman *did* look surprised when Nutty paid for the tent and then asked him to put it up *over* his cycle! "Over your cycle?" asked the puzzled salesman. "Yes, please!" grinned Nutty. "And can you make two holes in it?"

7. What a surprise poor Aunty Scofalot had, as she waited outside her house for Nutty. Suddenly, a strange white thing pedalled towards her! "Oh, my goodness – a ghost!" she gasped. "It's only me, silly!" called a voice.

8. How Aunty laughed when Nutty peeped his head out from under the tent. "I had to find some way to keep the rain out of my eyes – didn't I?" grinned Nutty. "You *are* funny, Nutty!" said Aunty.

CAMEL JIGSAW

A camel used to be the only thing that could cross a sandy desert, carrying people and goods, which is why it was known as *the ship of the desert*. It can store enough water in its hump to last for days and days.

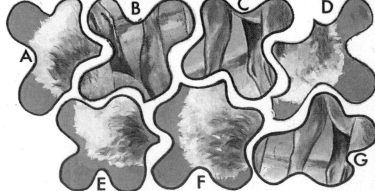

Now, two of these jigsaw pieces fit into the blank spaces in the big picture. Can you say which two pieces they are?

ANSWER:

Pieces 'B' and 'D' fit into the blank spaces.

Patch TO THE RESCUE

Patch wanted to play with a cat, one day. But the cat was afraid, so it ran away. She raced along to a nearby wood. Then climbed a tree as fast as she could.

But then the cat found she was stuck! Patch had an idea — the cat was in luck! He pulled some leaves down to the ground. Now the cat could land. It was safe and sound!

"You deserve a kiss," said the cat with glee. "Let's play a game — you and me." Patch did look pleased. He had found a friend. It had all come right for him in the end!

49

1. Tiger Tim and the Bruin Boys love playing football. "Try and kick the ball right past us!" grinned Tim to Jacko, in the garden, one day. Porky-Boy, who sometimes visits Mrs. Bruin's school, saw the boys playing.

2. Just as Jacko was about to kick the ball, Porky-Boy dashed out from behind a tree and kicked the ball right down the other end of the long garden! "Ha, ha! I've kicked the ball right past *all* of you!" he chuckled.

3. "What a horrid thing to do!" said Jumbo, when the boys found that their ball had been pierced by a spiky piece of bush. "I have an idea how we can teach Porky a lesson," said Tim. "Listen to my plan, boys."

4. One behind the other, the boys went into the kitchen. Tim put the burst ball under the cold water tap. How the boys chuckled when they saw the ball getting fat and round again. "Nearly ready now!" giggled Tim.

Tim and the burst ball

5. "We have forgiven you, Porky," smiled Tim, when he and his friends went back into the garden. "Come and play with us." "You are such a good kicker, Porky," added Jumbo. "See how hard you can kick the ball!"

6. "All right, I'll show you just how hard and how far I *can* kick it," boasted Porky. "Yes, do!" sniggered the boys. Nobody noticed their teacher, Mrs. Bruin, and Dr. Lion coming out of the house.

7. Dr. Lion's eyes gleamed when he saw that ball. "It's *ages* since I kicked a ball," he chuckled, as he bonked the ball. Up sailed the ball — and down splashed the water over the Bruin Boys. How Porky laughed.

8. But Porky stopped grinning when Tim explained how the ball came to have a hole in it. "I enjoyed my kick so much, here's some money to buy a new ball," smiled Dr. Lion. "Oh, thank you!" cheered the chums.

THE FOREST FRIENDS' FUNNY STILTS

1. Using two long, strong twigs, Teddy made himself a splendid pair of stilts. "Oh, can we have a go? Go on, *please!*" asked Charlie Chipmunk. "Oh, come on then, jump up," chuckled Teddy.

2. "Oooer! Be careful!" gasped Teddy, as Cuddly climbed on to his head. Then Cuddly helped Charlie up on to his head! "That's it. We are all on!" said Cuddly. "Off you go, Teddy. Quick, march!"

3. "Aren't we clever?" said Charlie, as the three friends wobbled past Sammy Squirrel's tree home. "Yes, but mind how you go!" laughed Sammy. "You will fall off if you're not careful!"

4. "Fall off, indeed!" grinned Teddy. "We are too clever to do that!" "Come on, let's cross that stream. The water is only shallow," said Charlie. "Well, er, all right. If you say so," said Teddy.

5. Suddenly, as the friends reached the middle of the stream, Teddy gave a strangled gasp – and disappeared! "Where's he gone?" said Cuddly, who was at the top of those long stilts.

6. The water was much deeper than the friends had thought! Teddy was *under* the water, gurgling and spluttering. "I'm down here, you silly things!" he tried to call. Of course, he couldn't.

7. The only thing for Teddy to do was to climb up one of those stilts. "You silly chipmunk, Charlie!" spluttered Teddy, when he reached the top of the stilt. "You said the water was *shallow!*"

8. "Well, I thought it was – sorry," said Charlie. Then he saw two herons. They had long legs, just like stilts. The kind herons said they would give the friends a ride. It *was* fun!

HAROLD HARE'S

1. "Come and see what the postman has brought, Dicky!" shouted Harold Hare, one morning. Dicky found his friend waving a letter from Cousin Haggis McHare, inviting them both to Scotland.

2. Without delay, Harold and Dicky packed their luggage and set off. And when they came to the Scottish border, there was Cousin Haggis waiting to welcome them. "Hello!" called Harold.

3. Haggis McHare lives in a cottage in the Highlands. He is very proud of his garden, where only *thistles* grow! "Everything is so different here," laughed Harold. How right he was!

4. Indoors, instead of making a nice cup of tea, Cousin Haggis made a nice pot of *porridge!* In fact, he seemed to have nothing else to eat except porridge, which is very filling.

holiday in SCOTLAND

5. "I wish things weren't *quite* so different here," Harold whispered to Dicky. But he cheered up when Cousin Haggis took them to the village hall to meet lots of Scottish friends.

6. The Scottish friends had prepared a feast. But as Harold walked past the huge table, all he saw was plate after plate of porridge. "I just can't eat any more porridge!" thought Harold.

7. But he needn't have worried. On his plate and on Dicky's plate were piles of *carrots!* "I know you like carrots just as much as I like porridge," said Cousin Haggis. Harold *was* pleased.

8. When he had eaten those carrots, Harold felt much better. The dancing began and Harold showed his friends the Topsy-Turvy Dance. "You really are a bonny hare, Harold!" said Cousin Haggis.

Dozey really is a dozey fellow, as you will see when you play this game. Take it in turns to throw a dice, then move your counter along that number of spaces. If you land on a picture, do what its message tells you. The first player to reach 'FINISH', wins!

DOZEY'S GAME

START

1 2 3 4 5 6

Miss a turn while Dozey eats his breakfast.

Dozey falls asleep on a see-saw. Miss a turn.

52 51 50 49 48 47

53

FINISH

At last, it is Dozey's bedtime!

41 42 43 44 45

40 39 38 37 3

46

Instead of reading his book, Dozey has fallen asleep! Go back five spaces.

On his way to the shops, Dozey stops for a nap. Go back three spaces.

13

14

12

10

9

8

7

11

Dozey falls asleep while ordering his shopping! Miss a turn.

15

16

17 **18**

19

20

Dozey goes for a boat ride. Speed on four spaces.

29

28

27

26

25

24

30

31

32

33

34

35

Dozey rests on a bench. Go back two spaces.

23 **22**

21

BOATS

THE CHEEKY KITTEN

What a surprise Benjamin Tabby Cat had, when the local pet shop delivered a tiny kitten to his house, one day. "Now I will have someone else to play with and look after," thought Benjamin, as his mistress, Emily, carried the kitten into the living-room. "I'm sure you two cats are going to get along just fine," smiled Emily, as she opened the kitten's cage and offered a friendly finger. But naughty Nippy scratched it! While Emily went to bathe the scratch, Benjamin strolled over to Nippy and said, in a very firm voice: "Either you behave, or I will take you back to the pet shop myself!" Nippy gave a naughty smile. He *liked* the pet shop. There were new faces to show off to and new fingers to nibble! Turning his back on Benjamin, Nippy ran straight up the living-room curtains! "Come down here – at once!" ordered Benjamin. Nippy did just that. But not the way Benjamin expected. Nippy jumped over Benjamin's head, pulling the curtains down with him!

Then, before Benjamin had time to catch him, Nippy scrambled up some other curtains at the far end of the room! Then he waved at Benjamin. ''What a silly old cat you are!'' he chuckled. ''You couldn't catch me for toffee apples!'' ''Well you cheeky young rascal!'' scowled Benjamin. But now it was Nippy's turn to get a surprise. Suddenly, the curtain he was holding on to, began to slip off its curtain rail. *Plip-plip-plip!* went the hooks, as the curtain began to sag. *''Oooh, er, save me!''* miaowed Nippy, as he slid down that curtain. Then *plop!* He landed in Emily's plate of porridge which was on the dining-room table! When Benjamin managed to stop miaowing with laughter, he took Nippy to the kitchen and firmly placed him in a bowl of nice, warm water. Nippy leaned over to bite Benjamin's tail, but slipped and bit the soap instead! ''Yeuck! That tastes horrible!'' sighed Nippy. ''Serves you right,'' said Benjamin. But he *did* feel rather sorry for the little kitten. He sat Nippy on a warm blanket and rolled him into a roly-poly shape. When Nippy's fur was nice and dry, Benjamin took him to a saucer of milk. ''Now share this with me, Nippy,'' smiled Benjamin. ''No pushing, mind — and no lapping *all*

the cream!'' Nippy looked rather ashamed with himself when Benjamin wrapped his warm tabby tail around Nippy's body. ''Well done!'' smiled Emily, when she saw how nicely the two cats were sharing. And, when Emily bent down to stroke his fur, Nippy didn't even *think* to nip at her finger. ''We have learned something today, haven't we, young fellow?'' whispered Benjamin. Then Nippy felt a funny quiver under his fur. It was his very first purr! When, later, Benjamin went to sleep in his big basket in the kitchen, he felt a warm, furry body under his blanket. ''Now who could be in my basket — apart from me?'' said Benjamin, with a grin. Nippy poked his head over the edge of the blanket. ''Er, I hope you don't mind me sleeping in here. But I have nowhere else to sleep,'' yawned Nippy. ''I don't mind at all,'' smiled Benjamin. ''As long as you don't nip me!'' ''Oh, I won't do that,'' grinned Nippy. ''I don't nip any more.'' ''I'm glad to hear that,'' said Benjamin. ''You may share my basket with me every night.''

Nurse Susan and Doctor David

1. Susan and David are sister and brother who work in their own pretend Toys Hospital. "This won't take long," Doctor David told a dolly, as he held her arm and pretended to feel her pulse.

2. David was just going to move on to the next patient, when a noise in the garden made him jump up. It was a loud whistling noise. "Just come and look what has happened!" he told Susan.

3. A dolly driver was lying on the path. He had just had an accident in his lorry. Peter Policeman was blowing his policeman's whistle. "I'm coming!" called David, rushing outside.

4. It didn't take Doctor David long to open his doctor's bag. "This dolly will have to go to hospital," he said. So Nurse Susan fetched a stretcher. "Well done, nurse. Fast work!" smiled Peter.

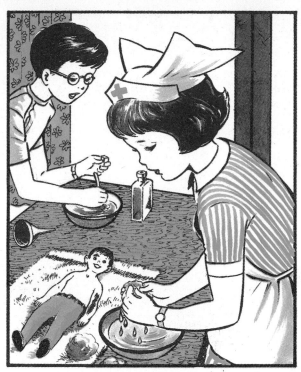

5. Off to the Toys Hospital went the dolly, carried by David and Peter. Nurse Susan hurried along beside the patient, holding his hand to make him feel more comfy. "Brave dolly!" she said.

6. Just as soon as they reached the hospital, Nurse Susan cleaned a rather nasty graze on the dolly's arm. Doctor David made a pretend medicine mixture with sugar and a little warm water.

7. "Drink this and you will soon begin to feel much better," said David, as he held the sugary water to the dolly's lips. Susan soon wrapped bandages round the dolly's grazed head and arm.

8. Later, Susan and David told Peter that the dolly would soon be well again. Peter was towing the lorry to the garage. "I'm sure the dolly will drive more carefully now," he said, waving goodbye.

Teddy Bear and the lost deer

1. One lovely warm summer's day, Teddy and the other bears decided to go on a picnic in the forest. ''I will find a picnic spot,'' laughed Teddy, leading the way.

2. He found a pretty glade where Mummy and Grandma laid out all the food on a table cloth. There were lots of nice things to eat and the bears couldn't wait to start.

3. Soon they were all sitting down having a lovely time, when Teddy spotted something. Coming towards them was a deer. ''Look,'' said Teddy. ''Mummy Deer is joining us.''

4. But when Mummy Deer got nearer, Teddy saw that she was very sad. ''I have lost my baby,'' she told Teddy. ''He was with me this morning, then he just ran away.''

5. Teddy did feel sorry for Mummy Deer. "We will help you look for your baby," said Teddy. So Teddy and the other bears went to search for the baby deer. They hunted all around, in the trees and in bushes. But the baby deer was not found in those places.

6. You see, while the bears were busy looking for the baby deer, the baby deer was busy eating their picnic. "Look!" called Teddy. "The baby deer is over there, eating our picnic." "Oh dear," said Mummy Deer. "I am sorry. He can be naughty!"

7. No-one minded really. The bears were too pleased to find the baby deer to be cross with it. "You must share our picnic," said Daddy Bear. Mummy Deer and her baby were pleased. "We will stay for a little while, thank you," said Mummy Deer.

8. When they had eaten a few sandwiches, Mummy Deer and her baby went back into the forest. "Thank you for your help," said Mummy Deer. "Bye, bye, try not to get lost again," called Teddy, as he and the other bears waved goodbye.

Wally Woo

1. Wally Woo is a rather plain-looking wooden train. But he is always bright and cheerful as he chugg-chuggs through Toy Town.

2. One day, Wally Woo was chugging through Toy Town, when suddenly – *whooosh!* Dasher Diesel whizzed past him, carrying lots of passengers. "Folk like *me* best, Wally Woo!" he called. "I'm much faster than you!"

3. Dasher, of course, runs on rails. He had to put on his brakes and come to a grinding halt when he saw the rails ahead of him had been flooded. "How can we get to Traintown now?" asked the passengers, climbing down.

4. "Just jump aboard Wally Woo. I will *float* across the water!" grinned Wally. "I don't need silly old *rails!*" "You are the most useful engine we know, Wally Woo!" cheered the Toy Town folk. Dasher never boasted again!.

farmyard counting

 How many
CHILDREN
can you count?

 How many
HORSES
can you count?

 How many
CHICKENS
can you count?

 How many
COCKS
can you count?

 How many
DUCKS
can you count?

 How many
PIGS
can you count?

These children are feeding the animals on their daddy's farm. Underneath this picture there are some counting questions for you to do. Write your answers in the blank squares beside each small picture.

ANSWERS: There are: 2 children, 4 chickens, 4 ducks, 2 horses, 1 cock and 3 pigs.

65

DREAMY

This is a story about a little mouse who likes to daydream. That is why he is called Dreamy...

1. Dreamy was lying beside the stream where he lives, dreaming as usual, when his mummy said: "Stop dreaming for a while and take this picnic to the park with you. A walk will do you good."

2. Dreamy would have preferred to sit and dream, but he did as he was told. Inside the park, Dreamy saw there was a speedboat for sale. It was only *twenty-five pence!* Dreamy *was* excited.

3. He closed his eyes – and began to dream again. He imagined he was an admiral, in charge of the speedboat he had seen. "What fun I'll have, travelling around the world!" he thought.

4. Admiral Dreamy climbed on to the speedboat and began to steer it through the water. "Here I come, landlubbers!" he called. "Full speed ahead!" Dreamy *did* feel important in his uniform.

5. Just ahead, Admiral Dreamy saw some other mice sitting in their little rowing boats. They did look annoyed when Dreamy whizzed past them. His speedboat made huge waves, which rocked the little boats. One tipped over!

6. Dreamy stopped dreaming, when the captain of the big speedboat said: "I expect you have come to buy my little speedboat." "Little?" said a puzzled Dreamy. He *did* look upset when he saw that it was a *model* speedboat!

7. "Oh, well, I should have known I wouldn't be able to buy a *real* boat for twenty-five pence!" thought Dreamy, as he walked through the park. Then he saw another notice. It said: 'FAIR AND BOATING LAKE'. Dreamy grinned.

8. This time, he didn't need to *dream* about going for a boat ride. He used his twenty-five pence to pay for a ride on the boating lake. "I knew I would make a good seaman!" laughed Dreamy, as he steered the little boat.

The fairy bells

1. The Queen of the Fairies, who loves the sound of bells, asked the Royal bell-maker to make lots and lots of bells. "Hang them up and colour them all blue," she told him.

2. Soon, the whole of Fairyland was hung with bells, which tinkled night and day. At first, everybody thought it was lovely. But, after a while, it became too noisy.

3. All the fairies and elves were tired and yawning. "Your Majesty, we like your bells, but we cannot sleep because of their tinkling," one elf told the Queen Fairy.

4. "Then I must move the bells," said the Queen. But where else could so many bells be put? "I know. We'll put them in the land of humans!" said the Queen, at last.

5. The Queen knew that the ears of humans are not made to hear fairy bells. By next morning, the world was covered with bells of blue and the humans called them *bluebells.*

6. Now, when the Fairy Queen misses the sound of the bells, she pays a visit to our bluebell woods. She might even let you hear them too, if you listen very hard.

The Lion on the egg

Long ago, a picture of a friendly lion used to be stamped on almost every egg you could buy. One morning, when a little girl named Sarah sat down to have her breakfast, her mummy put a delicious boiled egg in front of her. "I don't want a boiled egg!" said Sarah. When the lion on her egg heard Sarah say that, it began to cry. Its tears rolled over the side of the egg-cup, on to the floor – and out the kitchen door. When the lions on some eggs in the house next door saw the tears, they started to cry, too. Soon, all the lions on all the eggs in the town were crying, and great rivers of tears rushed down the High Street. Soon, the whole town was flooded and people had to go about in boats! When the Prime Minister heard about the flood, he looked very worried. "You must go and visit Sarah and find out why the lion on her egg made all the other lions on eggs cry," he told one of his aides. Mr. Stone, the Prime Minister's aide, could only reach Sarah's house by boat, of course. "Hello!" he called, as he rat-tatted on Sarah's kitchen window. "Is anybody there?" "Yes, *I* am," smiled Sarah. "Now, young lady," said Mr. Stone, "I understand that the lion on your egg made all the other lions on eggs, cry. It seems that you are the only person in the country who may be able to stop the lions crying and therefore stop the flood of tears from spreading world-wide." "Oh, yes, I can stop the lions crying," smiled Sarah. "In fact, I already have! You see, the lions only started crying because I wouldn't eat my boiled egg. Now I've eaten all my egg – and the lions have stopped crying." Mr. Stone was so pleased, he gave Sarah a special little medal. "The medal is for being the only person in the country who was able to stop a great flood!" said Mr. Stone. Sarah *did* feel important. And from that day on, she *always* ate an egg for breakfast.

1. Leo watched as Jimmy Mouse and some of his little friends played leapfrog, one day. "If I wasn't such a big, clumsy thing, I could join in, too," thought Leo. He *did* look unhappy.

2. Then Leo had a funny idea. "I know how I can make myself smaller," thought Leo. "I'll dig a hole – and stand in it!" But as Leo dug a hole, some earth flew up, then landed on Lonnie Lizard.

3. By the time Leo's hole was big enough for him to sit in up to his neck, Lonnie was covered with earth right up to *his* neck. "Now I'm small enough to play leapfrog," smiled Leo.

4. The next moment, Lonnie rushed up to Leo. Lonnie looked quite large from where Leo was. "I'll biff you on the nose, you clumsy, silly, thing!" cried Lonnie. "You covered me with earth!"

5.   Now Leo isn't very brave and doesn't like to be shouted at. "Save me!" he roared, jumping out of the hole. "Save *me*, you mean!" gasped Lonnie, when he saw he had been shouting at a huge lion!

6.   "Green animal, *please* go away!" stuttered Leo, covering his eyes with his paws. But Lonnie Lizard was already hurrying off. Just then, Jimmy came along to see why Leo was calling.

7.   "I thought if I made myself shorter, I could join in your leapfrog game. But I can't leap when I'm in a hole – and folk shout at me there!" sobbed Leo, as Jimmy and his friends listened.

8.   "Maybe you *can't* leap, but you can still join in our game," smiled Jimmy. "Into the hole you go, Leo." "This *is* fun!" chuckled happy Leo, as the tiny friends leaped over his large nose.

The May Queen

What an exciting day it was for little Bare Bear, when she was chosen to be Bear Green's May Queen! Kind Uncle Fred Bear used his best car to pull the May Queen's float along the High Street. Even Grizzly Bear stopped crying for a while. "Wave to everyone, Bare Bear," smiled Teddy. Now, the six small pictures drawn on the right show things that are hidden in the big picture. As you find each hidden object, put a tick in its box.

book

doll

pop-gun

Humpty-Dumpty

godlfish and bowl

potted plant

73

the magic cat

One evening, two fieldmice, one squirrel and one rabbit, came marching up Esmerelda Witch's garden path. On the doorstep, the friends met Cleo, the magic witch-cat. "Please, Cleo," asked one of the mice, "is Esmerelda in?" "She's not in to visitors, if that's what you mean," said Cleo. "She's busy cooking the supper. What do you want?" The squirrel gave a sigh. "We need a small spell to make us sleep," he said. "It's because of Oscar Owl, you see," said the rabbit. "Does he keep you awake?" asked Cleo. "Not as a rule," yawned the squirrel. "In fact, he usually puts us to sleep." "He has been telling us a bedtime story every night and when it's finished, we drop right off to sleep," squeaked a mouse. "But now he says he can't see to read us a story. His eyes are too tired – or something. So for us it's *terrible* – no story, no sleep!" "So we were hoping Esmerelda could cast a tiny spell and make us fall asleep," added the squirrel. Cleo thought for a moment, then her tail started to twitch. Suddenly,

Cleo's magic tail spun round and round, just like a windmill. At the same time, Cleo mumbled a few magic words. "Hookum-spookum, look out, eyes! Here come specs of a proper size!" cried Cleo. A few moments later, the friends heard a voice from the wood. "Yoo-hoo!" it said. "That's Oscar Owl calling us!" said the squirrel. "My magic must have worked," smiled Cleo. "Off you go now." The animals dashed back to the wood – and there they found Oscar with a brand new pair of spectacles on his beak! He was able to read to them once again.

PUZZLE TIME

1. Hector Hedgehog had three photographs taken of himself, to give to each of his friends. Now, one of these photos is slightly different from the other two. Look carefully and say which one it is.

A B C

2. What a tangle these balloons are in! Start at the letters A, B and C, and see if you can find out which string is tied to the balloons.

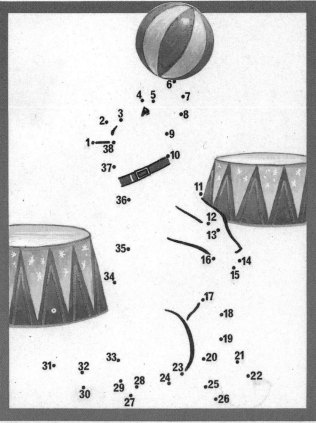

3. To see who is balancing this ball on its nose, join up all the dots from number 1 to 38. Then colour it.

4. Shade in all the dotted parts of this picture to see a creature that lives in the sea. What is it?

The King's Treasure

1. There once lived a king who loved his riches more than anything else in the world. In fact, even more than he loved his beautiful daughter, Jasmine. He had cellars stacked high with gold. "Only a very rich prince will be allowed to marry my daughter," he said.

2. Well, many princes, from far and wide, wanted to marry the beautiful princess. One day, the most handsome of them all came to the palace and immediately fell in love with Jasmine. "First, tell me what valuable things you own, Prince," said the king.

3. "The only riches I have is this sword," said the young prince. "With it, I will defend Your Majesty and all your riches." "My soldiers can do that!" said the proud king. The king's men sniggered behind their hands as the prince was told to leave the palace.

4. Now, Princess Jasmine had fallen deeply in love with the handsome young prince and would not marry any of the other princes who asked for her hand in marriage. Then the poor prince had an idea. He stained his skin brown and put on a long, dark brown wig.

5. Dressed in ragged clothes, the prince returned to the palace to work as a servant, so that he could be near the princess. But even Jasmine did not recognise him in his disguise. Then one day, the prince overheard robbers planning to steal the king's riches.

6. The prince rushed off to get his sword. Meanwhile, the robbers drugged the guards' food. When the soldiers were asleep, the robbers crept into the cellars. Suddenly, the prince rushed from his hiding place, shouting: "Follow me, men — after the thieves!"

7. The robbers, thinking they were going to be chased by many men, instead of just the prince and his mighty sword, fled from the palace, never to be seen again. "Young prince, you have indeed defended my riches," said the king. "You may have anything you wish." The prince smiled.

8. "I should like your greatest treasure," said the prince. "Your *daughter!*" "Of course, you may marry her," smiled the king. "Never again will I love riches more than people." So the prince and princess lived happily ever after.

WORM finds

1. Nellyphant, Joe, Tiny and Bob Robin, were in the garden of the Enchanted House when they saw Bernard Bloodhound. He seemed to be busy searching for something.

2. "What are you searching for?" asked Nellyphant. Bernard took them to the police station and showed them a notice. "Someone has lost a ring. So I am going to find it for them," said Bernard.

3. Bloodhounds are good at finding things. But it wasn't Bernard who found the ring, it was Worm. He *was* pleased when he saw the shiny thing lying on the ground near his home.

4. "My, I *do* look smart!" chuckled Worm. Silly thing – he didn't know he had found a *ring*. He thought it was a *hat!* Worm decided to go and show his friends how grand he looked.